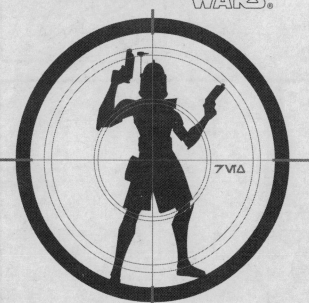

STAR WARS
THE CLONE WARS
WARS.

Contributing Artist: Paul E. Nunn

Dalmatian Press, LLC, ...
The DALMATIAN PRESS name, ...LC,
Franklin, Tennessee 37067. No ... ...out
the written permission from the ...

08 09 10 CL...

Use the grid below to draw a
CLONE
TROOPER.

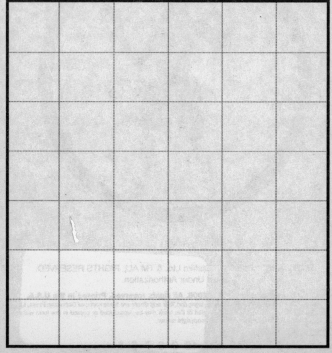

Dalmatian Press

How many CLONE TROOPERS do you see?

Your Answer _____

3

Answer: 7

Which Y-wing fighter is different?

A

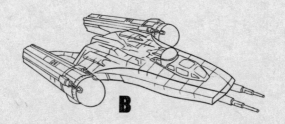

B

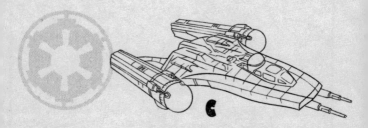

C

Your Answer _____

Use the grid to draw Anakin.

ANAKIN

Dalmatian Press

7

Finish Him!

General Grievous is part alien, part droid.
Draw the rest of him.

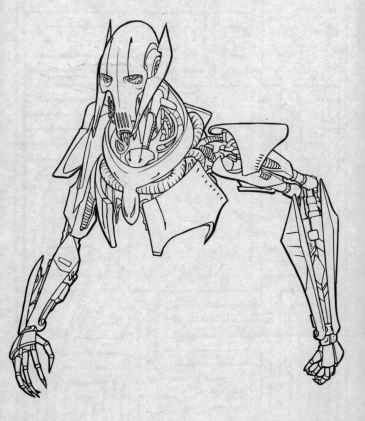

Help Obi-Wan track down
the General through the maze.

Grievous

START

FINISH

Dalmatian Press

Use the grid to complete the drawing of the

Clone Trooper

Dalmatian ❧ Press

Which clone trooper is different?

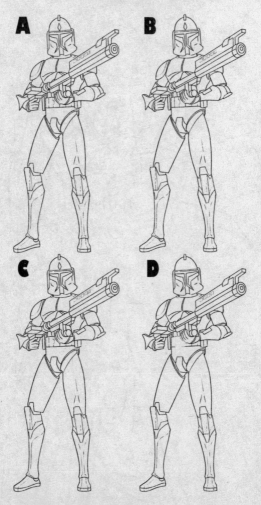

Your Answer _____

Answer: D

Which Obi-wan is different?

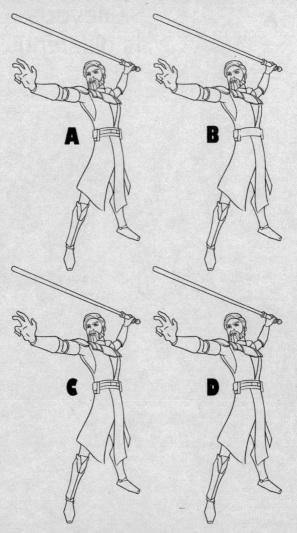

Your Answer _____

Answer: B

Which General Grievous is different?

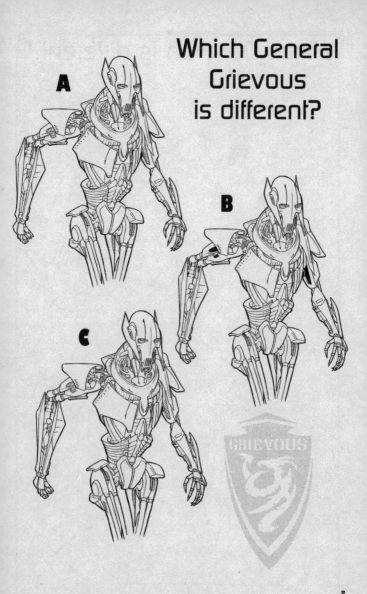

A

B

C

GRIEVOUS

Your Answer ____

Dalmatian Press

19

Help the Jedi track Dooku.

START

FINISH

COUNT DOOKU AND ASAJJ VENTRESS USE WHAT SIDE OF THE FORCE?

A. THE LEFT SIDE

B. THE SUNNY SIDE

C. THE DARK SIDE

D. THE BRIGHT SIDE

Answer: C

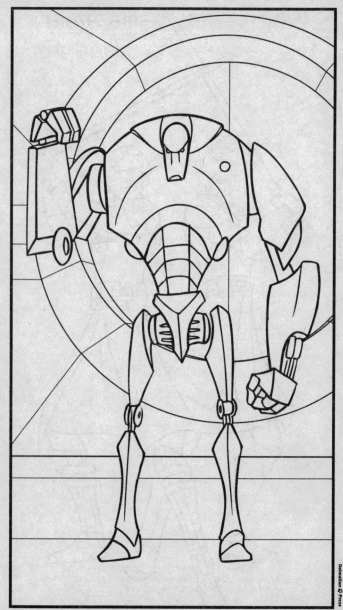

Which super battle droid is different?

Your Answer _____

Answer: A

How many words can you make from:

Asajj Ventress

• •

_____   _____   _____

_____   _____   _____

_____   _____   _____

_____   _____   _____

_____   _____   _____

_____   _____   _____

_____   _____   _____

_____   _____   _____

WHO AM I?

CLUE: Anakin Skywalker's Padawan learner in the Clone Wars.

A. YODA

B. AHSOKA

C. REX

D. SKY-GUY

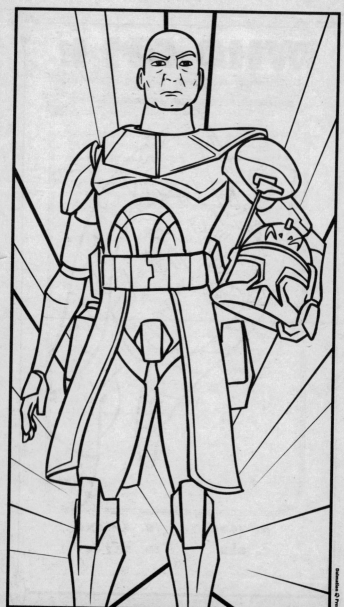

ATTACK OF THE CLONES

With a friend, take turns connecting the dots with a
single straight line, up and down or left and right.
When the connected lines complete a box, color that
box with your color. When all the dots are connected and
all the completed boxes colored, count the colored boxes.
The trooper with the most colored boxes will advance in the
Grand Army of the Republic to become an ARC trooper.

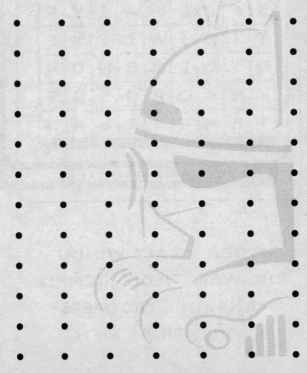

trooper A score ____ trooper B score ____

JEDI Word Search

Look forward, backward, up, down and diagonally.

M	P	A	C	S	E	H	J	T
L	A	N	A	K	I	N	N	R
P	L	C	J	R	N	T	U	O
V	P	X	E	R	A	E	H	O
B	A	C	D	W	W	Z	Y	P
T	T	D	I	W	I	S	Y	E
Q	I	O	E	M	B	N	O	R
K	N	A	Q	R	O	F	D	S
T	E	M	P	L	E	B	A	U

YODA   MACE WINDU

OBI-WAN   JEDI   TEMPLE

ANAKIN   TROOPERS

PALPATINE   SITH

BUILD-A-BOT

C-3PO needs repairs.
Draw a line to the part
that completes him.

A

B

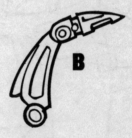

C

Your Answer _____

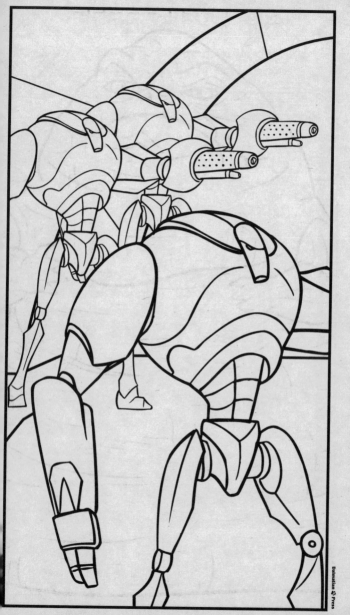

Dalmatian Press

Sith Lord Scramble

Unscramble the letters to reveal who is shown on the datapad screen.

RTADH NSYRUAT

_ _ _ _ _   _ _ _ _ _ _ _

Answer: Darth Tyranus

How do the Jedi teach their younglings?

A. They sit them in front of training computers and run simulations.

B. Yoda teaches the youngest, then Padawan learners are taken as apprentices by a Jedi Knight or Master.

C. They are given lots of books to read.

Your Answer ____

Dalmatian ♥ Press

YODA

Dalmatian ❧ Press

Sith Word Search

Look forward, backward, up, down and diagonally.

S	I	D	E	V	A	D	E	R
U	I	A	H	C	L	I	V	E
O	M	D	A	R	T	H	I	V
V	O	S	I	T	H	P	L	E
E	K	D	O	O	K	U	S	N
I	C	A	M	L	U	N	T	G
R	O	R	E	H	J	S	I	E
G	F	K	G	F	O	R	C	E
B	M	N	L	Y	T	W	E	D

EVIL SITH DARTH

SIDIOUS DOOKU

GRIEVOUS FORCE REVENGE

43

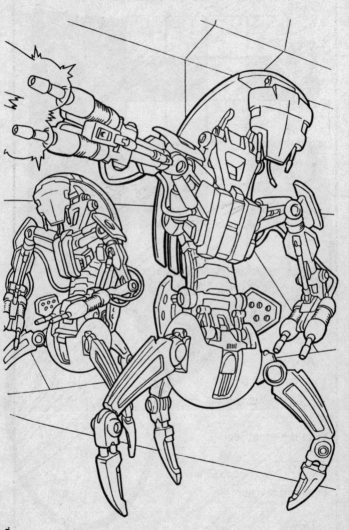

Yoda's Crossword

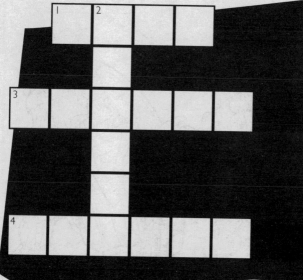

Across:

1. Yoda has long pointy _____ on the sides of his head.

3. Yoda is a great Jedi _____ .

4. _____ was once Obi-wan's Padawan learner.

Down:

2. Anakin Skywalker's Padawan learner.

Dalmatian Press

Dalmatian & Press

Anakin's Crossword

Across:

1. Because of the battles Anakin won in the Clone Wars, people called him a _____.
3. The color of Anakin's lightsaber.
4. Name of the Republic Senator Anakin married in secret after surviving the battle on Geonisis.

Down:

2. He was a Jedi Master to Anakin as a Padawan.

Answers: 1. hero, 2. Obi-wan, 3. blue, 4. Padmé

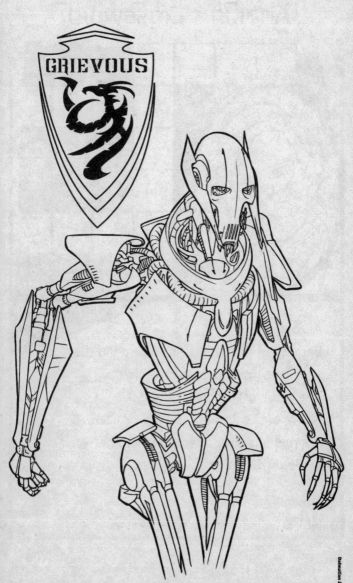

GRIEVOUS

Who Doesn't Belong?

Who was a Separatist in the Clone Wars?

A

B

C

D

Your Answer _____

51

Answer: C

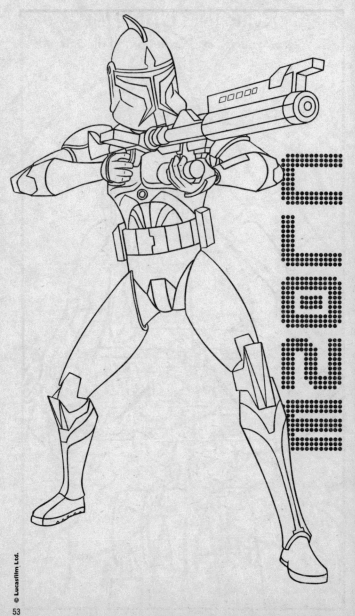

Rule the Universe

Draw yourself as a Dark Lord of the Sith.

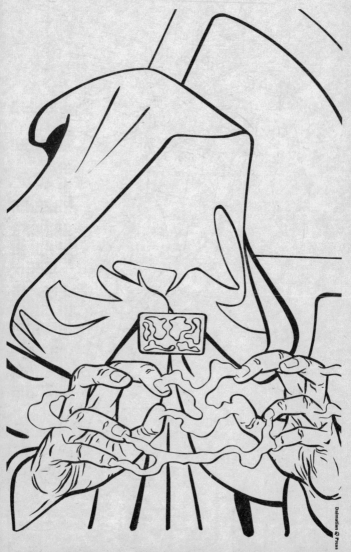

Which square completes the picture?

A   B   C   D

Your Answer _____

Dalmatian Press

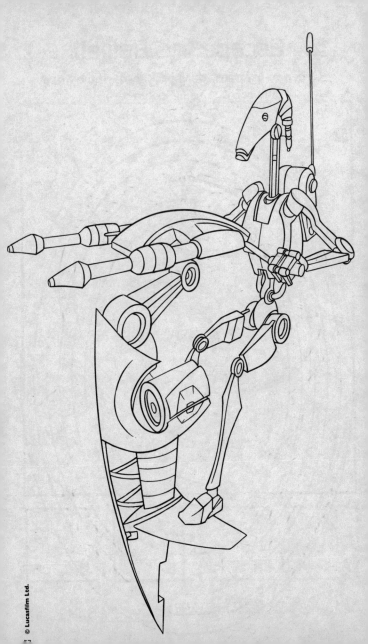

Escape the Battle!

Order your forces to fall back through the maze
and regroup to fight another day.

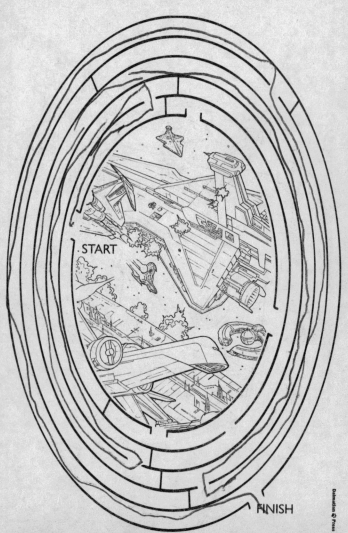

START

FINISH

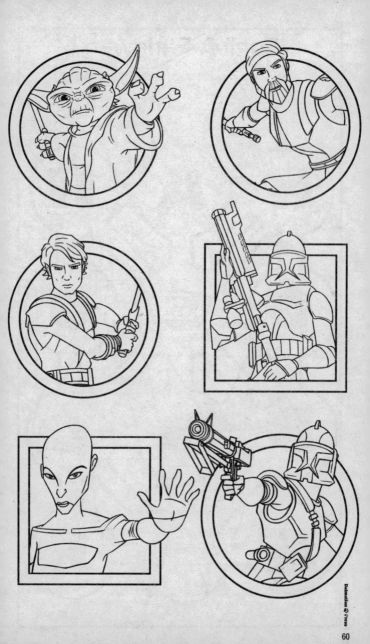

Spell-A-Padawan

Find your way through the maze spelling
the name of the person pictured at the bottom.

START

N A H
O S O
K R C
A E

FINISH

Answer: AHSOKA

Use the grid to draw Padmé.

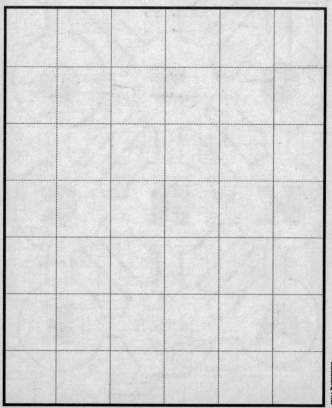

General Grievous' Getaway

Track Grievous through the maze.

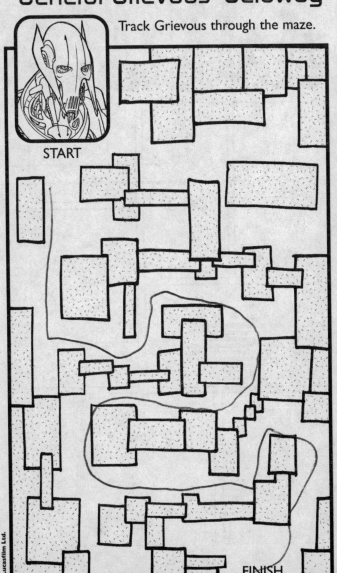

START

FINISH